Word Perfect Spelling

BOOK TWO

BY

RONALD RIDOUT

ILLUSTRATED BY

GEORGE W. ADAMSON, M.S.I.A.

Ginn and Company Ltd

BOOKS BY THE SAME AUTHOR

Write in English, Introductory Books 1 and 2 and Books 1-8: a new style of English Workbook providing a carefully graded course on understanding, using and writing English for all 6- to 12-year olds.

Better English, Introductory Book and Books 1-5: a complete English course from about 6-12 years; illustrated in colour.

English Workbooks, Introductory Books 1 and 2 and Books 1-8: a graded course in punctuation, spelling, vocabulary, comprehension and composition. The first two are intended for infants.

English Workbooks for the Caribbean, Books 1-8: a workbook course specially written for primary schools in the Caribbean; also suitable for immigrants; illustrated in colour.

English Now, Books 1-5: a complete course in magazine form for the less academic secondary pupil; illustrated in colour.

© RONALD RIDOUT 1957
Forty-fifth impression 1998
ISBN 0 602 20986 2

Published by Ginn and Company
Prebendal House, Parson's Fee, Aylesbury, Bucks HP20 2QY

Ginn on the Internet http://www.ginn.co.uk

Printed in Great Britain by Henry Ling Ltd, Dorchester

PREFACE

THE Introductory and eight main books of *Word Perfect Spelling* provide a systematic course in spelling and vocabulary for primary and secondary schools. Though in the first place it is correct spelling that they aim at, the books will at the same time help the pupil to gain complete mastery over the fundamental vocabulary needed by him at the various stages of his career.

Research has shown beyond dispute that the grouping of words in short lists according to common structural elements does facilitate their learning. The fact that words are held in the mind in certain patterns will, in both the short and the long run, enable them to be recalled more surely. In addition, it allows one key word to be used for unlocking many more. This, then, in the main, is the approach adopted, though other approaches have been used whenever they seemed to have a special contribution to make.

The course, however, does not end with the listing of words : it only begins there. The words have to be linked with the child's interests and brought to life by challenging activities. These activities are in themselves valuable aids to the teaching of English, but they have a vital function in improving spelling. They are based on the self-help principle whereby the pupil can hardly fail to get the right answer. This ensures that he will spell the word correctly when he writes it, and also use it correctly, so gaining the maximum benefit. For a child learns by doing, but he learns much more effectively by doing correctly.

The first few pages of Book Two are devoted mainly to revision of patterns met in Book One. In addition, through the exercises, revision of words and patterns is maintained throughout the book, thus ensuring a valuable sense of continuity. In all, 327 words from earlier books are revised.

Learning to spell in Book Two is still almost entirely based on the formation of correct habits, but some attempt is now made to draw the pupil's attention to the principles involved, as will be seen from pages 15, 17 and 22, for instance. New patterns are introduced at a steady rate and 639 new words are met, many of which are practised more than once. As more difficult words come along, greater emphasis is placed on meaning, especially in the new feature introduced on pages 27 and 42. For a more detailed discussion of the theory and practice of the course the teacher is referred to the Teachers' Manual of *Word Perfect Spelling*.

A set of diagnostic tests has been added to the Teachers' Manual, thus providing the teacher with a ready means of gauging the point at which any particular child or group should join the *Word Perfect Spelling* course.

HASLEMERE, 1976   R. R.

HOW TO LEARN
TO SPELL

1   Look at the word.   Say it softly.

2   Look at the word.   Say the letters.

3   Close your eyes.   Say the letters.

4   Look at the word to see
if you have spelt it right.

5   Write the word.
See if you spelt it right.

cake	weed
rake	need
shake	bleed
save	keep
cave	sheep
brave	creep
face	coat
race	boat
place	goal
lock	soon
clock	spoon
flock	boot

Which word goes with the picture?

Copy the picture, and choose the right word for it.

Can you spell all the words?

You have met them before, or words like them.

1. strong	white
2. warm	weak
3. wet	cold
4. black	fine
5. slow	under
6. like	push
7. pull	fast
8. over	hate

Strong is the opposite of weak ; over is the opposite of under.

Can you pair each word in the list with its opposite? Begin like this :

1. strong   weak
2. warm   ......

9. tall	thin
10. thick	happy
11. sad	short
12. open	dear
13. cheap	shut
14. far	always
15. asleep	near
16. never	awake

Now do the same with these.

You have met the words on this page before, or words like them.

Can you spell them all?

road	mice	ink	apple
goat	nine	bird	letter
desk	wood	one	umbrella
vest	stool	eight	postman
jug	football	horse	table
queen	clock	kitten	

Write the words in the same order as the pictures, and number them. You will then have put the words in the same order as the alphabet.

ABCDEFGHIJKLMNOPQRSTUVWXYZ

At school we sit on chairs
and work at desks.
We write with pens
but we draw with pencils.
Sometimes we work in pairs.
I like to draw pictures best.

write	pen	work	chair
like	pencil	school	pair
sometimes	desk	draw	picture

Fill these gaps with words from the patch.
Write out the complete sentences.

1. Bike rhymes or goes with —.
2. Hair rhymes with — and —.
3. — rhymes with straw.
4. — rhymes with kite.
5. When and then rhyme with —.
6. Fool and pool rhyme with —.
7. Instead of d in word, write k, and you get —.
8. The word desks means more than one —.

cap	cape	rob	robe
mat	mate	Tom	Rome
scrap	scrape	Ron	bone
pip	pipe	glad	blade
lid	slide	slim	chime
spit	spite	stop	slope

1. Make new words by adding e to each of these :
   rat hat rip tap bit pal

2. Make seven new words by putting each of these letters in front of ate : d, f, g, h, l, m, r.

3. Instead of h in hide write : r, s, t, w, br, sl.

4. Instead of p in poke write : j, w, sp, sm, br, ch.

5. Instead of b in bake write : c, l, m, r, sh, br.

6. Instead of h in hole write : p, m, tadp.

7. Instead of k in kite write : b, wr, wh, qu.

8. Instead of f in fire write : h, t, w, sp.

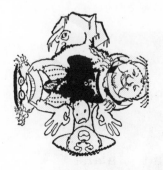

Mr East gave a feast.
Mr West did his best.
Mr North came not forth.
Mr South burnt his mouth
With eating a cold potato.

nor	eat	south	west
north	east	mouth	burnt
fork	feast	cloud	potato

1. Write these in full : N. S. E. W.
2. In front of east write : b, f, l.
3. Write burnt without the t.
4. Instead of w in west write :
   b, t, v, ch, cr.
5. In front of eat write : b, h, m, n, s, wh, ch.
6. Instead of f in fork write : c, p, st, Y, w.
7. Instead of l in loud write : cl, pr, al.
8. Instead of k in fork write : d, m, t, get, ty.

spell camp rush crust

shell lamp brush camping

smell stamp must spelling

1. Make new words by adding –ing to these :
   spell rush smell brush stamp rust

2. The word camp is used to make camping.
   Say what words are used to make these :
   rushing spelling telling stamping dusting

3. Add a letter and make rush into something to
   sweep with.

4. Add a letter and make rust into something to eat.

5. Write out all the words that begin with s.

6. If you add s to bell, you will make it mean more
   than one bell — bells. Now write each of these
   words so that it will mean more than one :
   shell lamp stamp crust ball

7. Write the seven words from the patch that can be
   built from these letters : E A U P S H M R T L L

bent	kicks	plums	sends
tent	picks	drums	belt
spend	stick	plump	test

Across

1. A stick becomes this when you bend it.
3. This word rhymes with best.

Down

1. This keeps a man's trousers up.
2. Campers sleep in this.

Across

1. You do this with money.
3. More than one kick.

Down

1. A long thin piece of wood.
2. More than one drum.

Across

1. More than one plum.
3. This word rhymes with kicks.

Down

1. Fat.
2. This word rhymes with bends.

tank	quick	fail	stand
sank	chicken	paid	snail
thank	ticket	plain	chain

1. `c h | | |`   This word rhymes with <u>rain</u>.

2. `f | | |`   The opposite of to succeed.

3. `| | | |`   This word rhymes with <u>laid</u>.

4. `| | | | |`   The opposite of <u>slow</u>.

5. `| | | | |`   It carries its house on its back.

6. `| | | | | |`   You buy this to go on a train.

Write these words with the letters in the right places:

7. `a n k t`   This holds water.

8. `a s n k`   Went under the water.

9. `a n d s t`   To be on two feet.

10. `a i n p l`   This word means the same as <u>clear</u>.

11. `e n i c k c h`   A bird.

12. `a n t h k`   This word rhymes with <u>sank</u>.

left	hand	its	hair
right	foot	doll's	fair
bright	head	shoes	pretty

Write these sentences in the same order as the numbers:

This is the doll's right foot.
This is its right arm.
This is its left hand.
This is its left shoe.
This is the doll's head.
This is the doll's right hand.

Copy this carefully:

Mary has a very pretty doll.
It has fair hair
and bright pink cheeks.
Its dress is blue
and it has red shoes on its feet.
It can walk and talk.

brain	waiting	fond	bark
again	painting	pond	part
wait	sailing	second	barn

1. Take away the first letter of <u>drain</u> and you get <u>rain</u>.

   Now take away the first letter of each of these words, and write down the word you get :

   <u>brain</u> <u>again</u> <u>part</u> <u>laid</u> <u>bark</u> <u>snail</u>

2. Write the words from the patch that rhyme with :

   <u>dark</u> <u>pond</u> <u>start</u> <u>drain</u> <u>darn</u>

3. The word <u>wait</u> is used to make <u>waiting</u>.
   What words are used to make the following?

   <u>barking</u> <u>painting</u> <u>failing</u> <u>standing</u> <u>thanking</u>

4. Instead of r in <u>rain</u> write : p, g, br, ch, dr, pl.

5. Instead of p in <u>part</u> write : d, c, t, st, sm.

6. Make new words by adding -ing to these :

   <u>wait</u> <u>paint</u> <u>rain</u> <u>part</u> <u>darn</u> <u>faint</u>

act	help	plant	year
acted	helped	planted	tomorrow
add	wash	ask	yesterday

Make these sentences mean that all the things happened yesterday. Begin like this:

1. Yesterday I added up this sum.
2. Yesterday Jill acted ....

1. Tomorrow I shall add up this sum.
2. Tomorrow Jill will act in a play.
3. Tomorrow Jane will help her mother.
4. Tomorrow John will wash his bike.
5. Next year Mr Black will plant a rose bush.
6. Next year I shall act in the school play.
7. Tomorrow we shall help wash up the tea things.
8. Next week Mary will ask Miss Green about it.
9. Next week we shall plant the apple trees.
10. Next year I shall walk to school.
11. Next term I shall start Book Three.
12. I shall finish in a moment.

There are forty children in our class.
This morning we have a spelling test.
We write the words down on our paper.
Then the teacher writes them on the blackboard.
We see how many words we can get right.

write	class	morning	many
word	paper	forty	children
spelling	teacher	right	blackboard

Let's make sure.

(1)

lend	boat	clap	doing
went	load	glad	going
spend	goal	plan	mending

(2)

case	hold	sharp	from
chase	told	mark	frost
tame	bolt	market	frog

(3)

dĕar	paid	saw	dinner
year	laid	draw	supper
clear	mother	morning	happy

My name is John. I am nine years old.
I have a bedroom of my own at home.
I ride my bike to school.
I am never late.

ride	–	riding	live	–	living
bite	–	biting	give	–	giving
write	–	writing	love	–	loving
chase	–	chasing	have	–	having

Write the words ending in e from which these have been made :

1. living   3. giving   5. chasing   7. making
2. having   4. writing   6. saving   8. shaking

Add -ing to the following words. Remember that the silent e at the end will disappear.

9. love   11. chase   13. dive   15. wave   17. hope
10. ride   12. make   14. rise   16. hate   18. shine

Write these, putting in the missing words :

19. I make a cake. I am — a cake.
20. You ride a horse. You are — a horse.
21. The sun shines. The sun is —.
22. He chases the dog. He is — the dog.
23. Daddy drives the car. Daddy is — the car.
24. The boys write. The boys are —.

 It is not safe to cross the road
when a car is coming.
I must stop, look right,
look left, and then right again.
Then if there is nothing coming,
I can cross the road.
It always pays to take care.

cross	looking	take	straight
crossing	listening	safe	right
crossed	always	care	around

1. Say the word take and hear the long a sound.
Then say the words in the list below and write
out the five that have the same long a sound.

    make   pack   slap   name   stand
    back   safe   always   bang   again

2. This time write the five words that have the long
i sound that you can hear in right.

    might   skin   stick   strip   pile
    split   fine   like   stripe   spill

glass – glasses	dress – dresses
bush – bushes	bus – buses
box – boxes	flash – flashes
inch – inches	match – matches

To make a noun mean more than one (plural) we usually add s : girl—girls, boy—boys.

But if a noun meaning one only (singular) ends with a hissing sound like s, sh, x, ch, we must add es to make it plural : glass—glasses, stitch—stitches.

boxes	brush	dishes	patch	classes
box	brushes	dish	patches	class
inch	foxes	kiss	thrushes	watch
inches	fox	kisses	thrush	watches

Make two lists. In one write all the singular nouns from the ring. In the other write all the plural nouns. Begin like this :

Singular Nouns : box, inch, ...

Plural Nouns : boxes, inches, ...

earn	does	never	join
early	goes	clever	point
learn	toes	river	boil

1. Choose from the patch the opposite of :

late   always   stupid   part

2. Write these sentences, putting one word from the patch for each underlined part.

   (a) He came to school before the proper time.

   (b) Make the tea when you see the water bubble.

   (c) At no time cross the road without looking.

   (d) Ann has broken the sharp end of her pencil.

   (e) I will put together these two railway lines.

3. Write the words from the patch that rhyme with :

soil   clever   learn   coin   joint

4. Write the plural of these nouns :

dress   inch   bush   box   toe   joint

5. Write the singular of these nouns :

inches   foxes   brushes   matches   points   toes

Andrew lives in a new house.
Upstairs there are three bedrooms.
His bedroom has two windows,
a bed and a chair. There is a rug
on the floor. Downstairs there is
a large living-room and a kitchen.
Andrew goes out of the back door
to play in the garden.

door	air	bedroom	upstairs
poor	stair	garden	downstairs
floor	chair	kitchen	windows

Write these sentences, putting in the right words
from the patch.

1. Rich is the opposite of —, and upstairs is the
   opposite of —.
2. Floor and poor rhyme with —.
3. There are two — in Andrew's bedroom.
4. Andrew sleeps in a — and plays in the —.
5. The six words ending in r are —, —, —, —, —,
   and —.

A. Each of these words is made up of two smaller words. The word <u>pancake</u> is made up of <u>pan</u> and <u>cake</u>. Copy the lists, and put the small words in boxes at the side of each big word. Begin like this :

1. bedroom | bed | | room |

1. bedroom	11. snowball
2. butterfly	12. someone
3. cannot	13. sunshine
4. doorway	14. tablespoon
5. grandfather	15. teaspoon
6. outside	16. teatime
7. pancake	17. timetable
8. policeman	18. today
9. postman	19. downstairs
10. playground	20. wireless

B. Now write twenty sentences to say how the words are made up. Begin like this :

1. *The word bedroom is made up of bed and room.*

because	hear	nearly	reading
before	hearing	easy	behind
below	speaking	cheating	least

1. Make new words by putting be– in front of each of these :

    low   long   side   cause   came

2. Make new words by adding –ing to these :

    hear   fear   reach   eat   beat   teach

3. Instead of h in <u>h</u>eat write : b, m, n, s, ch, gr.

4. Instead of h in <u>h</u>ear write : d, f, g, n, r, t, y, cl.

Find the right words from the patch.

5. [b _ _ w]   The opposite of above.

6. [c _ _ _ _ g]   Not playing fair.

7. [_ _ y]   The opposite of hard.

8. [_ _ _ _]   You do this with your ears.

9. [_ _ _ _ _]   The opposite of most.

10. [_ _ _ _ _ _]   Almost.

11. [_ _ _ _ _ _]   The opposite of after.

12. [_ _ _ _ _ _]   The opposite of in front of.

run   –   running   chop   –   chopping

rub   –   rubbing   swim   –   swimming

drip – dripping   scrub – scrubbing

whip – whipping   clap   –   clapping

When you add –ing to words like those in the patch, you have to double the last letter and then add –ing. Make new words by adding –ing to these :

1. swim   4. stop   7. drop   10. plan   13. knit

2. sit   5. scrub   8. beg   11. tap   14. whip

3. win   6. shut   9. skip   12. slip   15. spin

Whipping is made from the shorter word whip. Write the shorter words that these have been made from :

16. sitting   19. scrubbing 22. letting   25. fanning

17. hitting   20. hugging   23. slapping 26. hopping

18. dripping 21. clapping   24. cutting   27. whipping

28. See if you can make twenty smaller words with the letters of SCRUBBING.

A foolish young person called Bright
Was flying a very big kite,
   But the wind was too strong
   And he held on too long,
And soon he was right out of sight.

right	long	soon	young
sight	strong	fool	person
bright	held	foolish	flying

1. Write the five words from the list below that have the same long o̲ sound as you can hear in fool.

boot	strong	room	you	sour
long	moon	person	young	two

2. Write the five words from the list below that have the same e̲ sound as you can hear in held.

help	kept	these	sent	people
she	sleep	left	we	fell

thin	fattest	robber	chopper
thinner	biggest	robbed	chopped
thinnest	wettest	dinner	slipper

When you add –er, –est, or –ed to words like thin, fat, big, wet, rob, chop, you have to double the last letter and then add –er, –est, or –ed.

1. Make new words by adding –er to these :
   thin   fat   big   rob   chop   slip

2. Make new words by adding –est to these :
   big   thin   wet   hot   red   slim

3. Make new words by adding –ed to these :
   rob   stop   trot   slip   skid   scrub

4. Can you learn this by heart and write it out?

Good ! Better ! Best !
Let us never rest
Till our good is better
And our better, best.

slow	cross	soft	cleverly
slowly	crossly	softly	bravely
wisely	neatly	rarely	quickly

Choose the right words from the patch to fill the gaps. Write out the complete sentences.

1. He talked so — that we could not hear him.
2. He never makes a blot. He writes very —.
3. John ran — and so won the race.
4. Mrs Smith — speaks crossly. I have heard her speak — only once in my life.

Slow tells us about a person. (He was a slow worker.) Slowly tells us about an action. (He worked slowly.) Slow is an adjective, and slowly is an adverb. Make adverbs by adding -ly to these adjectives :

    5. brave   7. loud   9. bold   11. soft
    6. quick   8. clever   10. smart   12. quiet

Write the adjectives from which these adverbs come :
13. crossly 14. softly 15. wisely 16. safely 17. clearly

There are five of us
in our family.
I have a sister called Mary
and a brother called Peter.
My own name is Susan.
Then there are Mummy
and Daddy.
Granny lives with us too.
My uncle and aunt live
in the next street.

mummy	mother	brother	uncle
daddy	father	sister	aunt
granny	grandmother	children	family

Children is made from the shorter word child.
Skipped is made from the shorter word skip.

Write the shorter words these are made from :

1. children
2. sunny
3. funny
4. knitted
5. fatter
6. shopper
7. slipper
8. winner
9. thinnest
10. reddest
11. greatest
12. knitting
13. whipped
14. roasted
15. planted
16. planned

Write the word out with its meaning. The page numbers tell you where to find the words, so that you can check your spelling.

1. `h` `|` `|` `y` The opposite of sad. (page 2)

2. `|` `|` `c` `|` `l` `s` You use these to draw with. (4)

3. `|` `e` `a` `|` The opposite of dear. (2)

4. `|` `e` `e` `|` The wife of a king. (3)

5. `|` `a` `|` `|` The opposite of asleep. (2)

6. `|` `i` `|` `|` A man smokes this. (5)

7. `|` `|` `e` `r` A man who robs. (24)

8. `|` `|` `|` `g` The opposite of weak. (23)

9. `t` `|` `|` More than one toe. (18)

10. `|` `|` `|` `y` Short for grandmother. (26)

11. `|` `|` `e` Your mother's brother. (26)

12. `|` `|` `p` `p` `|` `|` A tap is often doing this. (22)

13. `|` `|` `l` `y` In a neat way. (25)

14. `|` `|` `t` `|` In a soft way. (25)

15. `|` `|` `|` `y` Almost. (21)

16. `|` `|` `|` `|` `|` More than one match. (17)

17. `|` `|` `|` `|` `|` `|` `|` The opposite of up-stairs. (19)

18. `|` `|` `|` `|` `|` `|` More than one child. (26)

19. `|` `|` `|` `|` `|` You write on this. (13)

20. `|` `|` `|` `|` `|` `|` The day after today. (12)

Let's make sure.

thing	quick	which	slow
(4) bring	quiet	what	crow
string	loud	who	own

dive	need	much	softly
(5) alive	bleed	such	quickly
along	steer	lunch	bravely

patch	matches	hoped	pence
(6) match	glasses	smoked	dance
catch	brushes	blamed	dancing

One morning we were awake early. My brother and I dressed quickly. The sun was shining. Soon we were chasing each other in the garden.

sack	loaf	pound	salt
packet	coal	trousers	fruit
shoes	bacon	chocolates	bread

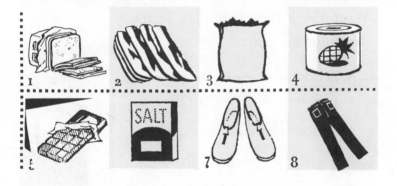

Draw the pictures. Write one of these under each :

a sack of coal   a packet of salt

a loaf of bread   a pair of trousers

a pair of shoes   a pound of bacon

a tin of fruit   a bar of chocolate

Put in the right words from the patch.

   9. pepper and —   11. — and butter

  10. socks and —   12. — and eggs

diver	baker	farmer	docker
driver	reader	butcher	porter
miner	teacher	worker	grocer

Write the sentences, putting in the words from the patch.

1. A person who works is called a —.
2. A person who drives is called a —.
3. A person who reads is called a —.
4. A — is a person who dives.
5. A — is a man who makes bread.
6. A — is a man who sells meat.
7. A — unloads ships.
8. A man who digs coal is called a —.

9. A — sells tea, soap, butter and bacon.
10. A person who teaches is called a —.
11. A — is a man who owns a farm.
12. A man who carries luggage is called a —.

self	hunt	race	selfish
myself	hunter	racer	racing
yourself	blunt	place	bunch

Make new words by putting these in front of self :

1. my   2. your   3. him   4. her   5. it

6. Instead of r in race write : f, l, p, pl, sp, tr, gr.

Write the singular of these nouns :

7. hunters 8. races 9. bunches 10. inches 11. lunches

Write the plural of these nouns :

12. place   13. inch   14. driver   15. butcher   16. dress

Write these sentences, putting in :

myself, yourself, himself, herself, itself.

17. John washed — under the tap.

18. Mother picked — a bunch of roses.

19. I cut — on a shell, racing down the beach.

20. You must drive — hard if you want to win.

21. The bike righted — and then went on without its rider !

Sunday	before
Monday	after
Tuesday	between
Wednesday	today
Thursday	yesterday
Friday	holiday
Saturday	tomorrow

1. The day after Tuesday is —.

2. The day before Wednesday is —.

3. The day before — is Monday.

4. If today is Thursday, tomorrow will be —.

5. If today is —, tomorrow will be Wednesday.

6. If yesterday was Tuesday, today must be —.

7. The day between Tuesday and Thursday is —.

8. At our school — is a holiday, and so is —.

9. Sun. is short for Sunday, and Mon. is short for —.

10. Tues. is short for —, and Wed. is short for —.

11. Thurs., Fri., Sat. are short for —, —, and —.

12. — is the only day with nine letters in its name.

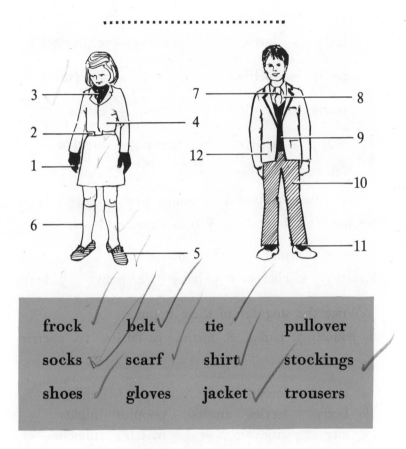

frock belt tie pullover

socks scarf shirt stockings

shoes gloves jacket trousers

Each number goes with one of the words.

Look at the numbers and see what they point to.

Then write twelve sentences, beginning like this :

     1. These are the girl's gloves.

     2. This is the girl's —.

lady	— ladies	cherry	— cherries
baby	— babies	berry	— berries
pony	— ponies	city	— cities
story	— stories	lorry	— lorries

To make the plural of nouns like <u>lady</u> and <u>berry</u> we have to change the y into i and add –es.

Write the plural of these nouns :

1. city   2. cherry   3. baby   4. pony   5. berry

Write the singular of these nouns :

6. ponies   7. ladies   8. lorries   9. fairies   10. cherries

berries	lorry	story	poppy	night
berry	lorries	stories	poppies	nights
city	cities	—	match	matches

Make one list of the singular nouns in the ring and another of the plural. Begin like this :

<u>Singular Nouns</u> : berry, city ......

<u>Plural Nouns</u> : berries ......

born	merry	light	morning
corn	jelly	lighter	muddy
corner	jolly	bright	tonight

Write the words from the patch that rhyme with :
1. holly   2. berry   3. corn   4. bright   5. Horner

Write the singular of these nouns :
6. mornings   7. corners   8. jellies   9. berries

Write the plural of these nouns :
10. jelly   11. berry   12. night   13. lady   14. city

15. Instead of c in <u>corn</u> write :   b, h, t, w, ac.
16. For l in <u>light</u> write :   f, m, n, r, s, br, fl, sl.

<u>Muddy</u> is made from the shorter word <u>mud</u>.   Write the shorter words that these are made from :
17. sunny 18. foggy 19. faddy 20. furry 21. gummy

Make new words by doubling the last letter of these words and adding y :
22. mud   23. dad   24. mum   25. fog   26. fur

No. 1

No. 2

No. 3

No. 4

No. 5

Mr Jones	bridge
Mrs Smith	street
Mrs Davies	lives
Mr O'Henry	doctor
Dr McDonald	number

The people live in these houses in the same order as the alphabet.

Mrs Davies lives in Number One, because D comes before J in the alphabet. Mr Jones lives in Number Two, because J comes before M. And so on.

Draw the houses and put the right names on them.

Then write five sentences, saying who lives in each house. Begin like this:

1. Mrs Davies lives at 1 Bridge Street.
2. Mr Jones lives at . . . .

cry	carry	hurry	flies
cries	carries	hurries	dries
cried	carried	hurried	tries

Rewrite sentences 1–6. Two are done for you.

1. The baby is crying. (The baby cries.)
2. The blackbird is flying over the bush.
   (The blackbird flies over the bush.)
3. Andrew is trying hard to do his work.
4. Helen is carrying her mother's basket.
5. Mother is drying the dishes very quickly.
6. Alice is frying the bacon.

Change these so that everything happened yesterday. Begin like this : 7. *Yesterday I hurried home.*

7. Tomorrow I shall hurry home.
8. Tomorrow I shall carry mother's basket.
9. Tomorrow I shall dry the glasses quickly.
10. Next week I shall fry the bacon.
11. Soon I shall copy the next sentence.
12. In a moment I shall tidy the shelf.

grow	know	few	could
growing	knowing	dew	would
grew	knew	blew	should

1. Instead of r in <u>row</u> write : s, l, t, bl, gr, kn, sl.

2. Instead of n in <u>new</u> write : d, f, p, bl, gr, ch, st, cr, kn.

3. Can you learn the poem by heart and write it out?

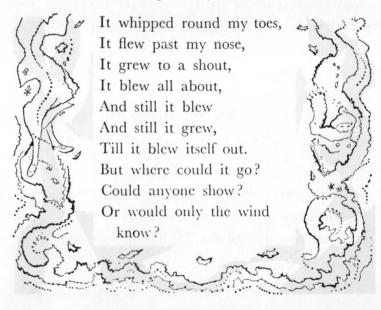

It whipped round my toes,
It flew past my nose,
It grew to a shout,
It blew all about,
And still it blew
And still it grew,
Till it blew itself out.
But where could it go?
Could anyone show?
Or would only the wind
know?

o'clock	twelve	seven	year
hours	fortnight	sixty	week
minutes	month	twenty-four	half

1. There are — days in a week.
2. There are — minutes in an hour.
3. Four weeks make a —.
4. Two weeks make a —.
5. There are — hours in a day.
6. A year has — months.
7. The small hand marks the —.
8. The big hand marks the —.

Write these times in the same order as the clocks, working from left to right :

The time is eight o'clock.

It is four o'clock.

The time is half-past two.

It is half-past four.

turn	dead	hang	curl
burn	ready	bang	church
hurt	already	sang	death

Can you put the first list of words in alphabetical order ? Burn comes before hurt, because b comes before h in the alphabet. Then hurt comes before turn, because h comes before t.

But suppose that two words begin with the same letter, like curl and church in the last list ? You must then look at the second letters. Thus, church comes before curl, because h comes before u. Then curl comes before death, because c comes before d.

Now write all four lists in alphabetical order, and number them 1 to 4.

Then put these lists in alphabetical order :

    5. church, burn, curl

    6. week, month, year, minute

    7. sing, song, sang

    8. matches, churches, patches, catches

song	care	firm	oblong
long	fare	first	square
strong	spare	third	circle

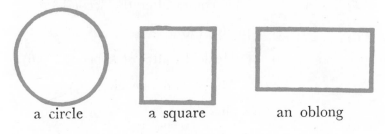

a circle   a square   an oblong

1. Draw an oblong. Write in it all the words that end in –ong.
2. Draw a square, and write in it all the words ending in –are.
3. Draw a circle, and in it write the four words that have –ir– in them.
4. Instead of s in <u>song</u> write : str, obl, al, wr.
5. Write the four words that rhyme with rare.
6. Write the four words that rhyme with wrong.
7. Instead of c in <u>care</u> write : d, r, sh, f, st.
8. Write the singular of : songs, fares, squares, inches.

1. [ ] [o] [s]   More than one shoe. (page 29)

2. [ ] [u] [n] [ ]   Not sharp. (31)

3. [ ] [ ] [ ] [e] [r]   Man who carries luggage. (30)

4. [ ] [ ] [ ] [y]   The day before Tuesday. (32)

5. [ ] [ ] [ ] [i] [e] [s]   More than one lorry. (34)

6. [ ] [r] [ ]   You pay this to go on a bus. (41)

7. [ ] [i] [r] [ ]   This comes after the second. (41)

8. [ ] [w]   Not many. (38)

9. [ ] [ ] [ ] [o] [r]   He looks after sick people. (36)

10. [ ] [ ] [ ] [ ] [ ]   More than one city. (34)

11. [ ] [ ] [ ]   Not alive. (40)

12. [ ] [ ] [ ] [ ]   They keep your hands warm. (33)

13. [ ] [ ] [ ] [ ]   Covered with mud. (35)

14. [ ] [ ] [ ] [ ] [ ] [ ] [ ]   Two weeks. (39)

15. [ ] [ ] [ ] [ ]   To go quickly, or hasten. (37)

16. [ ] [ ] [ ] [ ] [ ] [ ]   More than one child. (26)

17. [ ] [ ] [ ] [ ] [ ]   Not very often. (25)

18. [ ] [ ] [ ] [ ] [ ]   The opposite of ugly. (10)

19. [ ] [ ] [ ] [ ]   The opposite of most. (21)

20. [ ] [ ] [ ] [ ] [ ] [ ]   Most thin of all. (24)

21. [ ] [ ] [ ] [ ]   It means the same as clear. (9)

Let's make sure.

(7)

found	Sue	hush	cream
pound	blue	crush	dream
hour	true	thrush	steal

(8)

dirt	oil	tool	use
skirt	boil	tooth	using
shirt	soil	teeth	used

(9)

foggy	because	great	none
clapped	before	their	some
spinning	beside	only	many

Every morning my mother wakes me at half-past seven. I wash myself and clean my teeth. Then I dress and brush my hair. After that I go downstairs.

For extra work

(1)

family	played	fresh	throw
families	stayed	flesh	follow
puppies	enjoyed	next	hollow

(2)

hearing	flame	either	beautiful
heard	shame	neither	warm
beard	blame	nobody	lovely

(3)

word	snow	clown	knew
world	sleet	brown	knitted
worth	storm	flower	knotted

(4)

marry	stone	riding	write
merry	stove	dancing	wrote
hurry	whole	driving	wring